As the newly appointed chief of the East Orthopedic Trauma Service at Massachusetts General Hospital, I was called to the emergency department to examine a patient who had a severe open tibia/fibula fracture of his lower leg—the foot dangling without support and hanging on only by a sleeve of back-sided muscle.

I recall telling the surrounding medical staff, "If he has sensation over the bottom of his foot, I can put the leg back together with an external fixator. If there is no sensation, he would be better served with an amputation."

Everyone in the room stopped and held their collective breath as I pricked the sole of his foot with a pin. And with the words, "I feel it!" commenced the long, painful, and ultimately triumphant journey of Christopher Lockwood.

—Daniel O'Neill, MD
NASA Bone & Joint Specialists, Houston, Texas
Former Chief of the East Orthopedic Trauma Service
Massachusetts General Hospital

WHY THE CANE?

A true story about the support and advice that enabled a man to regain a level of activity he thought would not be possible after a traumatic injury

Christopher G. Lockwood

Why the Cane?
Copyright © 2019 Christopher G. Lockwood

ISBN: 978-1-63381-172-0

All rights reserved. No part of this book may be reproduced in any form or by any electronic or mechanical means, including information storage and retrieval systems, without permission in writing from the author, except by a reviewer, who may quote brief passages in review.

Designed and produced by:
Maine Authors Publishing
12 High Street, Thomaston, Maine
www.maineauthorspublishing.com

Printed in the United States of America

Dedication

Cindy Lockwood
1946–2017

With love and sadness, I dedicate this book to my late wife, Cindy, who passed away in November 2017 after a truly heroic battle with pancreatic cancer. Cindy held our family together in the days and months following "the accident," which is the focus of this book. I thank her for her unselfish and loving care of me and our family when our world was turned upside down and forever changed.

Table of Contents

Preface

"The accident"—that's how our family refers to it. It's a defining event that serves as a milestone for us. "Was that before or after the accident?" we sometimes ask. A number of years after it, my daughter would joke, "Do you ever think there will be a time when we'll say, 'Do you remember the time that Dad was hit by the car?'" That's a reflection of the Lockwood sense of humor, which has helped us make it through tough times.

It's been thirty years since "the accident." At various times I've thought about writing about it, but I've held back for a variety of reasons: time, or the lack thereof, or the risk of sharing deeply personal experiences involving my family and me. Also, as bad as the accident was, far worse things have happened to other people and they often have more heroic achievements.

Why now have I decided to write this book? There are several reasons. When I retired from my full-time job in 2015, after serving as executive director of the Maine Municipal Association for 36 years, I had the enjoyable challenge of deciding how to spend my newfound time.

I had worked with Maine Authors Publishing in 2013 to publish *The Tennis Ball Trees*, a children's story I had written a few years earlier. I thoroughly enjoyed this experience and looked forward to pursuing my interest in writing on a part-time basis.

In early 2016, Jane Karker, the president of Maine Authors Publishing, arranged for me to meet with Lee Heffner, a writer's coach. Lee invited me to discuss various topics I was considering. I mentioned several ideas, including another children's book, a book about "the accident," and a book about my decision to retire and the retirement process.

When she provided feedback, Lee was emphatic that I needed to write about "the accident," at the very least for myself and for my family. She provided very helpful suggestions about the writing process and encouraged me to pursue my interest in writing.

There is certainly a cathartic element for me, but my overwhelming reason for writing the book is to share the incredibly helpful advice and support I received during my rehabilitation. It won't sound or seem to be particularly extraordinary, but it has provided me with a framework to regain a level of activity I never thought would be possible in the aftermath of the accident.

Hopefully this book is not about me. If this book helps even one person regain a meaningful level of activity after a traumatic injury or serious health challenge, it will have been worth the time and effort I took to write it.

Prologue

This afternoon after work I was playing catch with Joel in the yard. We've worked out a system where he retrieves the ball if it goes past me very far. Nate returned from a tennis lesson in Waterville. He let me use his racquet (actually it's my racquet, but he had it restrung). I hit Joel a few pop flies with the tennis ball—using my racquet. It felt so good to hit the ball. I just can't bring myself to accept not being able to play tennis again—I love the sport so much—but I know realistically that the doctors don't think there's any way it'll ever happen.

Journal—Christopher Lockwood
October 24, 1989

CHAPTER 1

The Accident

Oh, what I would give for an ice chip. It's the most important thing in my life at this moment. I cannot think of anything I would rather have than a mouthful of ice chips. If someone offered me a choice of a million dollars or a mouthful of ice chips, I would choose the ice chips.

How absurd, but this is the truth. Even a few days later, it would be difficult to imagine such an extreme need to relieve myself of an unquenchable dryness in my mouth, but this is how I found myself in a surgical recovery room at Massachusetts General Hospital.

It's January 9, 1989, and my life has been turned upside down. The events of the past week swirl through my head. A ski outing gone awry, but far more than that. A life-changing experience. No one in my family would ever be the same.

I've just been through yet another twelve-hour surgery—this time a "free flap" operation conducted by the plastic surgery team. My mouth is parched, but instructions have been given to restrict any liquids, since I might need to be whisked back into the operating room at a moment's notice in case the skin and tissue grafts start to be rejected. As I lie in my hospital bed praying for a nurse to come by to swab my mouth, my thoughts go back to that fateful day.

January 2—the last day of the kids' Christmas vacation. I awoke at 6:00 a.m. to finish loading the van with our ski gear. The single-digit temperature sent a chill through my bones, but I knew how much my youngest sons Aaron (12) and Joel (6) were counting on this outing. This would be Joel's first downhill skiing of the season, and Aaron was looking forward to a day's skiing with his friend Christopher, who was back in Maine from Florida for a week's visit. With the van warmed up, we started off from our home in Hallowell for the nearly two-hour drive to Sugarloaf USA, stopping to pick up Christopher's mother, Sue, who was staying in town. We planned to meet Christopher and his grandfather at Sugarloaf.

Snow began to fall an hour into the trip. I checked the road at several points, but the traction remained good. As we approached the small town of Kingfield, I remarked to Sue on how beautiful the woods and fields appeared in the falling snow. We were on schedule and certainly had time to make a brief stop in Kingfield to pick up a replacement lens for Sue's ski goggles. Sue didn't want to hold us up, but I insisted that it would not be a problem. I was able to park off the road across the street from the store. I pressed a button to release the rear hatch door and got out and walked to the back of my van to assist Sue in checking her gear. My world would never be the same.

Without warning, a car careened in my direction. I had a momentary glimpse of the car a split second before it hit me and drove me up into the air, catching my left leg on the bumper of the van. Although everything happened in a matter of seconds, it still replays in my mind, frame by frame in slow motion (like the Zapruder film frames of the JFK assassination). I saw my left leg shattered. It was absolutely gruesome and gory—I will never forget the sight (nor unfortunately will Aaron, who, as I found out later, got out of the van after it had been pushed forward by the car that hit me and came back to see his father sprawled on the ground in a pool of blood).

Bedlam ensued. I lay on the icy, cold pavement as people scrambled to tend to me. I would later learn that an EMT came from the store across the street with blankets and administered emergency first aid, together with a doctor from Pennsylvania who was headed to Sugarloaf. Years later I still have people tell me they were in the line of traffic that backed up for miles the day of the accident.

For some amazing reason, I never lost consciousness, but I was in utterly indescribable pain. As I would learn later, my left leg had been 90% severed. I knew I had been terribly injured, but I didn't know how badly. Would I die?

The Sugarloaf Ambulance/Rescue crew arrived on the scene within twenty minutes. Ron Morin, Paramedic, the head of the ambulance service, oversaw getting me onto a stretcher and into the ambulance to warm up and decide how to proceed. I asked him

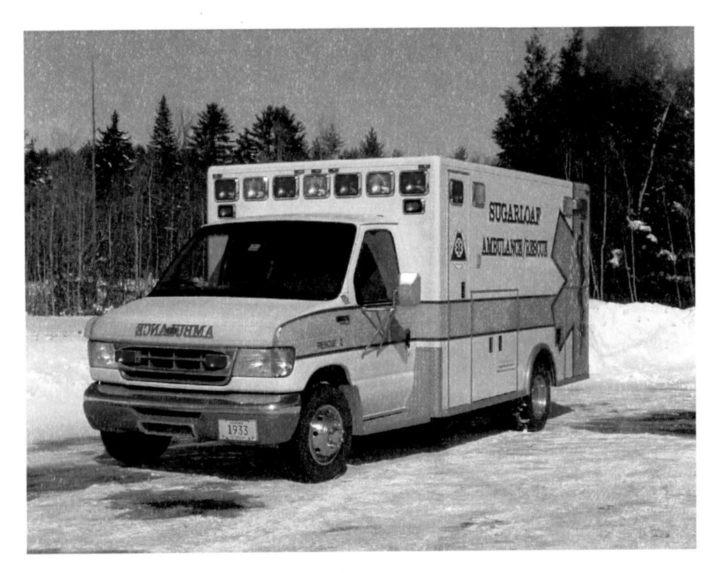

Sugarloaf Ambulance/Rescue vehicle

Sugarloaf Ambulance/Rescue Logo

if my injuries were really bad. He said yes—to which I replied that I wanted to be taken to the best medical facility possible. He said that would be Mass General in Boston. I asked him how I would get there, and he said he would need to arrange a helicopter. This was before Maine had a LifeFlight helicopter service, so I thought he might need to arrange for a National Guard helicopter. Given my professional relationship with Maine Governor Jock McKernan, I told Ron to contact the governor if he needed to. At that point, he laughed and said this wasn't a political thing, but he got my point.

I was very concerned about Aaron and Joel, and I didn't want Sue and the boys to travel with me or the emergency vehicle. I was also concerned about keeping my wife, Cindy, informed. She was at work at Slates Restaurant in Hallowell. Ron said he would dispatch his crew to take me to the local hospital in Farmington about 20 minutes away to get me stabilized while he went back to his headquarters to try to arrange for a medical helicopter from Boston.

The ambulance crew, headed by Ron's wife, Becky, was wonderful—they provided encouragement while trying to make me as comfortable as possible. I had only been at the hospital for a short time when word came to load me back in the ambulance to drive to the airport in Lewiston–Auburn (L–A) to meet the helicopter flying in from Boston. I asked the crew to be in touch with my wife to let her know what was happening. They assured me that they would.

The trip to the L–A airport took about an hour given the difficult driving conditions. As we approached the airport, the ambulance crew could see the helicopter landing. It was snowing heavily. The operator of one of the hangars very kindly agreed to allow the ambulance to pull into the hangar so I could be transferred under cover to the special stretcher for the helicopter. The ambulance crew extended their best wishes and assured me they would be in touch with Cindy.

The helicopter medical crew took over and got me situated with earphones, so they could communicate with me during the flight. They kept me heavily medicated, but I still was in a state of total disbelief and fear at what might lie ahead. I had never been hospitalized before and had never undergone major surgery. My thoughts swirled: How bad was this? Was I in danger of dying? Were Cindy and the kids OK? Would I ever play tennis again? Had I left things in order? What medical procedures would I face?

The medical team had arranged for an ambulance to be waiting as we landed on the helicopter pad near the Charles River. I recall screaming in pain as my leg was jolted during the short drive to Mass General when we hit bumps and took corners.

The rescue crew was able to remove Lockwood's L.L.Bean boots without cutting them. He still uses the boots.

CHAPTER 2

Arrival at Mass General

It was late afternoon by the time I arrived at Mass General. I was taken to a bay in the emergency department where I waited to be seen. I was terrified of what might lie ahead. Everything was unknown. I was alone and in totally uncharted territory. I could hear screaming from a patient in an adjacent bay.

Within a short period of time, Dr. Brian Ridge, the chief resident vascular surgeon, introduced himself to me. I had two main concerns:

I wanted to be sure that Cindy knew I wanted her to stay in Maine to provide support and comfort to our four children and not risk driving to Boston in the storm. Dr. Ridge concurred with this and assured me he would talk with Cindy and keep her informed throughout.

I also said it was important for him to be "straight up" with me—not to sugarcoat things. I needed to know what I was facing. I told him my preference would be to try to save my leg if there was any chance I could have reasonable function. He told me it didn't look good. My left leg was 90% severed close to my knee. I could undergo a dozen or more surgeries over a period of several years and still end up losing my leg.

A medical team surrounded my bed, squeezing my toes and pricking my foot with a pin, but there was no response. I later learned Dr. Ridge and Dr. Brian O'Neill, the chief resident orthopaedic surgeon, had left to scrub in for an above-the-knee amputation, given the location of the injury.

Shortly before I was taken to the operating room, one of the other doctors changed the question. He asked if I could move my toes. Ever so slightly, I was able to move my toes. The staff passed this information on to the doctors in the scrub room. Given Dr. Ridge's earlier conversation with me, they changed plans from doing an amputation and instead initiated the first of what would be many surgeries to try to save my leg.

Just as I was being wheeled to the operating room, John Madden (not the football coach), my long-time friend who now lived about an hour away in New Hampshire, showed up to reassure me and wish me well. It was comforting to know that John was at the hospital and to realize that family and friends were being contacted.

The initial surgery went for twelve hours. Dr. Ridge was true to his word. He called Cindy around 2:00 a.m. to give her an update. Initially the orthopaedic team installed an external fixator (a Hoffman device), like a large Erector Set, into my left leg to keep my leg stabilized for the next few months, when I would undergo extensive plastic and bone surgery to try to save my leg. The device was screwed in near my knee and just above my ankle, essentially serving as an external skeleton to keep my leg in place. After the orthopaedic team had completed its work, Dr. Ridge and his team took a vein from my upper right leg to use in "revascularizing" my left leg.

In hindsight, it's remarkable to consider the serendipity of the exchanges which led to the decision to try to save my leg: the conversation I had with Dr. Ridge regarding my preference, the off-hand change of the question by one of the doctors to ask if I could move my toes, and the decision to pass that information along to the scrub room. If any of these things had not happened, the outcome would have been totally different.

CHAPTER 3

The Beginning of a Long Journey

This would be the first of many surgeries. When I regained consciousness in the intensive care unit, I could hear my brothers Steve and Bert on either side of my bed. They had come in overnight from upstate New York and Ohio. My arms were tied down and I had a breathing tube down my throat, so I couldn't speak or move my arms. I tried to signal with my eyes that I wanted my forehead swabbed, but they couldn't understand what I was trying to tell them. I could hear them exchanging various incorrect guesses between them, to my frustration, until a nurse came in. One of them said, "We think our brother is trying to tell us something." The nurse looked and easily understood that I wanted my forehead swabbed with a damp washcloth.

The previous week we had given our kids the game *Pictionary*, a charade-type game, for Christmas. When I was finally able to speak after the breathing tube was removed, I told my brothers that I thought of *Pictionary* as they were striking out trying to guess what I was signaling.

In the following days I was taken to the operating room for debridements, surgeries to remove dead tissue. The next major surgery would be a "free flap," a live tissue transfer performed by the plastic surgery team headed by chief resident Dr. Jeffrey Fearon. My primary care nurse Maureen was assigned the task of briefing me on this surgery. She told me it was important for her to be direct. She noted that when I had arrived at Mass General I had been hit by a car. Maureen told me that after the free flap surgery I would feel like I had been hit by a *truck*. The surgery would last about twelve hours. The plastic surgery team would take muscle tissue from my right side below my armpit as a filler to replace the soft tissue on my left leg which had been destroyed in the accident. They would then take a skin graft from my upper right thigh and place it over the transplanted muscle tissue on my left leg.

This would be very delicate surgery. I would need to be able to be brought back into the operating room on a moment's notice if there were any signs of rejection of the tissue transplant or skin graft. I would not be able to have any liquids or food for forty-eight hours. This is how I found myself in the recovery room after the surgery, cajoling my nurse to give me a mouthful of ice chips rather than just swabbing my mouth. I was actually successful in my persuasion!

The days after the free flap surgery were very difficult. In addition to no fluids or solids for forty-eight hours post surgery, the donor sites for the skin graft on my right thigh and the muscle tissue transfer from my right armpit were very painful. I had a fever and skin rash. It was excruciating each time the dressing and bandages had to be changed—that's when I realized my preference is to "rip the bandage off quickly"!

By the time I was able to have something to eat and drink, my mouth was full of canker sores. Four days after the surgery, the doctors changed the dressing on my left leg. The good news was that the free flap looked good, but it hurt a great deal when they moved my leg. I also experienced ongoing muscle spasms, and occasionally I would feel a jolt run down my leg, as if nerves were suddenly activating. This jolting would continue for several months.

Fortunately, there was no rejection of the tissue transfer or skin graft and the free flap surgery was deemed a success by the plastic surgery team. I was very relieved and allowed myself to believe the worse was behind me. This was clearly an important milestone, but I was not aware of the many more challenges that lay ahead.

CHAPTER 4

A World Turned Upside Down

I was forty-two years old at the time of the accident. I was in my tenth year as executive director of the Maine Municipal Association, a statewide voluntary membership organization that provides an array of professional services to municipalities throughout the state. Cindy and I had four children—Sarah (18), Nate (15), Aaron (12), and Joel (6). Our home in Hallowell was a short distance from my office in Augusta and about a three-hour drive from Boston.

I was physically active, playing tennis on a regular basis, golfing, cross-country and downhill skiing, and hiking, as well as doing a wide variety of chores and projects around the house. Tennis was by far my favorite sport. My son Nate was on the high school tennis team, and we had started to play against each other on a fairly even basis. I also had a couple of friends with whom I played singles several times a month.

I had a reputation for being very even-tempered. Certainly anger was not a characteristic that friends or colleagues would associate with Chris Lockwood. This would be very relevant as the coming months would play out.

This was the first time Cindy and I found ourselves in an intense medical situation. Our world had been turned upside down and was swirling at breakneck speed. For Cindy—so many people to notify, stabilizing the family, keeping in touch with the doctors, deciding when to travel to Boston, keeping up with the basics of meals and everyday life, on top of the trauma and terrible uncertainty of what might lie ahead.

On a practical level, one of the first things Cindy did was to purchase two medium-sized spiral notebooks, one for her and one that she brought to me to have by my bedside at Mass General. This proved to be invaluable for Cindy in making notes about conversations with doctors, offers of help, reminders of things to do, keeping track of phone numbers and contact information, etc.

For me the notebook served many purposes—a journal, names of doctors and nurses, notes about conversations with doctors, keeping track of visitors and gifts, etc.

Our sudden immersion in a medical crisis also taught us important lessons. During my initial time in the hospital, I was inclined to accept whatever was proposed as the right course of action. I certainly was thankful that I had been taken to Mass General, but I discovered along the way that it would be important for me to be my own advocate. The more I could learn, the better I could work with my doctors and nurses. I learned the importance of asking questions and exploring options.

My first experience came a few days after my arrival at Mass General. While the major focus was on my left leg, I also had other injuries, including numbness in my right arm (perhaps resulting from hitting the pavement with my elbow when I was struck by the car). My doctors discussed the idea of operating on my right arm at the same time I would be under anesthesia for one of the surgeries on my left leg. Although I was somewhat inclined to take advantage of a "two-for-one" surgery, I decided to delay having anything done to my arm with the thought of tackling one thing at a time. As things turned out, the numbness in my right arm faded over the next few weeks. It was a good lesson in listening to my instincts.

The lessons learned from this foray into dealing with a major health crisis would equip us well for health issues we would face in future years.

Throughout my stay at Mass General, I had a tremendous amount of support. I was flooded with cards, flowers, books, boxes of candy, and other gifts. I had a steady stream of visitors. Cindy and the kids made trips from Maine almost every weekend. One particular gift I recall was a radio headset with an antenna. I got a stiff neck one evening, as I had to cock my head at a certain angle to get the radio broadcast of the hockey game between Harvard and St. Lawrence University, my alma mater.

When one of my visitors inquired about Chris Lockwood's room number, the woman at the front desk said she would tell him if he would tell her who Chris Lockwood was. She said that I had received more cards from across the country than almost any other patient they had ever had.

I also received letters and cards from many prominent federal, state and local officials from Maine, given my position as executive director of the Maine Municipal Association. They expressed shock at the accident and offered support and well wishes.

My administrative assistant at Maine Municipal Association had only worked with me for a few months before the accident. She received many calls from municipal officials and colleagues inquiring about my condition and asking about my interests so they might send along a card or gift. She explained that she wasn't sure about my interests, but that she knew I liked *Milky Ways.* As a result, I received a very large supply of *Milky Ways*, including a floral bouquet with six king size *Milky Ways* among the flowers! I didn't have much of an appetite and my mouth was filled with canker sores after the battery of surgeries, but I had a great supply of *Milky Ways* and other goodies to offer my kids when they visited. As a side note, it would be several years before I regained my love of *Milky Ways.* I think there was too strong an association with the hospital and the surgeries!

CHAPTER 5

A Long Hospital Stay

My initial stay at Mass General spanned six weeks, multiple surgeries, and nine different roommates. I tried to maintain a positive focus, but it was difficult as I experienced ongoing pain, the prospect of more surgeries, and various setbacks. Little things certainly helped, such as looking forward to phone calls each morning from Cindy and the kids, receiving cards, flowers, and small gifts, and having a fairly steady stream of visitors. My first shampoo (given in my bed by my nurses) allowed me to feel halfway human again.

I learned the importance of grabbing on to small gains, celebrating these little victories. One such example was learning how to use a simple device I was given—a short pole with a coat hook at the end—to use in getting myself dressed, pulling up clothing I couldn't otherwise reach given my injuries.

On the other hand, I also experienced the frustration of not being able to reach the rolling table with my belongings after it had been pushed away by a hospital attendant.

At times it would be almost impossible for me to imagine ever being able to even get out of bed or on my feet again. This was certainly the case the first time the medical staff had me place my leg over the side of the bed as an initial phase of eventually getting me to be able to stand using a walker. I thought I would pass out as the blood rushed to my foot. I could not fathom that I would ever be able to stand, let alone walk again. I found it helpful to keep these thoughts in mind as I gradually made headway—to hold on to the small gains I had made, especially when I would get discouraged after I experienced a setback.

In writing this book, I reread the journal I attempted to keep after the accident. This brought back many difficult and painful memories I had blocked out or had faded over time. I'd always been squeamish around medical procedures and equipment. Indeed, during my stay at Mass General, my wife reminded me to be sensitive to this point—that others might not delight at having me pull back my bed sheet to show them the large external metal fixator that was screwed into my leg.

The next major surgery would be a bone graft to be performed by the orthopaedic team. Bone tissue would be taken from a donor site on the back of one of my hips and placed in my lower left leg to replace the bone tissue that had been destroyed in the accident. The goal would be for the transplanted bone tissue to grow and unite with the bones to which it was grafted. This would be an essential step to allow me to bear weight and begin to regain some use of my left leg. My journal entries provide a glimpse of this experience:

1/31/89—Tuesday

Today is the day for the bone graft operation. I've signed the necessary authorizations and called Cindy and the kids.

Got back from OR mid afternoon—in absolutely excruciating pain. The nurses said the operation was successful, but I'm in terrible pain—felt nauseous—thirsty—couldn't urinate, so had to have a catheter put in (11 p.m.). Didn't get much sleep—on morphine shots. My left hip cramps up if I cough or try to move at all—it's brutal. Didn't feel up to talking to Cindy or anyone.

2/1/89—Wednesday

Dr. Fearon, the chief resident plastic surgeon stopped by—said things went OK.

Dr. O'Neill & the orthopaedic team came by—they said the operation went well, but we've got to monitor for infection. If there is infection, they'll have to do debridement and redo the bone graft. I'm really concerned about that. I'd hate to go through this again.

I tried to get into a wheelchair, but couldn't do it. My hip is in terrible pain and tightens up. Had to have another catheter—not very pleasant. I'm sort of down mentally after having made such headway.

My roommate (#6) is on the phone a lot and has lots of visitors. Fortunately this afternoon he spent a lot of time in the lounge to give me a break.

Frank Colcord visited tonight. We had a really good talk—it was great to have a chance to share my feelings.

2/2/89 (30 days since I arrived)—Thursday

Didn't sleep too well. Vincent's TV was on late. It took Maureen (my nurse) a long time to respond to my call light. I finally was able to urinate on my own!

The orthopaedic team pulled the drains and changed my dressing this a.m. It hurt a lot to move the leg around.

Stepped down from morphine to Percocet pills—the hip and leg still hurt a lot. I couldn't get out of bed.

Maureen and Beth changed the dressing tonight. They did a good job, but it's very tender. The ankle is quite swollen. Maureen wrapped it with an ACE bandage, but I had to have her take it off in the middle of the night.

I had a very difficult time in the days after the bone graft surgery. I continued to be in quite a bit of pain, and my red blood cell count dropped, which was concerning. I was very weak and pale. This occurred over a weekend when my regular doctors and nurses were not available. I was scared and worried about the broader implications. I was given several pints of blood and was relieved when Dr. O'Neill assured me this was not a critical situation, although they would continue to monitor things.

At one point in between surgeries I was well enough to take advantage of an invitation to have dinner in a wood-paneled boutique room on an upper floor. This was intended to give patients a change of pace from having meals in their hospital rooms. My nurse helped me get into a wheelchair and I set off on my own for the elevator, enjoying a small modicum of independence. That sense of independence ended abruptly when I encountered a wooden threshold at the entrance to the boutique. I needed to wait until someone would come along who could push the wheelchair over the threshold—a harbinger of what might lie ahead.

I finally was notified that my health insurance would no longer cover my stay at Mass General. It would be several weeks before my next surgery when the doctors would remove the external metal fixator and place my leg in a long plaster cast as they waited to see if the bone graft had been successful. Cindy and I were quite nervous about having me return home without any transitional care or rehab. Fortunately, arrangements were made for me to be transferred to Spaulding Rehabilitation Hospital, which was affiliated with Mass General and located a few blocks away on the Charles River.

When I was transferred to Spaulding, I was primarily confined to a wheelchair. I had just started using crutches, but I was very weak (having lost 40 pounds as a result of the various surgeries) and I could not bear any weight on my left leg due to the external fixator and the recent bone graft surgery. It was clear that I needed both physical and occupational therapy to assist me in regaining strength and learning techniques for basic functions, such as going up and down stairs safely with crutches, getting in and out of a shower without bearing any weight on my left leg, and other basic activities.

During my two-week stay at Spaulding I was surrounded by people who had far worse injuries than I. I was placed in a double room on the head injury floor due to the lack of beds in other units. I had trouble getting sleep given the noise and screaming. At my physical therapy sessions, there were amputees on either side of me. In one way, I felt fortunate, but I was still dealing with tremendous challenges—whether I would need more surgeries, whether I would ultimately lose my leg, how I would deal with a permanent partial disability due to the destruction of nerve and muscle tissue in my left leg, etc.

I had a fair amount of latitude at Spaulding to leave the facility with the assistance of visitors. I enjoyed the change of pace to go to an outside restaurant, but it was exhausting for me to get in and out of a car and to use my crutches to get around. It was a relief when I got back to my hospital bed. These outings gave me a sneak preview of what might lie ahead upon my discharge.

When I met with my assigned doctor at Spaulding for my discharge meeting, she apologized that I had not received more in the way of counseling to assist me. As she explained, in an ironic way, I was one of the healthier patients at Spaulding, but I had still incurred major injuries. This would be a paradox with which I would struggle in the coming months and years. Given the extent of my injuries, I appeared to be doing well after having undergone a battery of surgeries, but my world had been turned upside down.

Could I regain a normal level of activity? What is the new normal? Skiing wasn't a passion for me, but did I need to downhill ski again or accomplish some major achievement, like climbing a mountain or running a marathon? What will people think? Magazine covers and news stories certainly dramatize the Herculean feats some people manage to accomplish after major incidents or wartime injuries. I did not have a frame of reference by which to gauge what would be appropriate in my situation.

CHAPTER 6

Returning Home

Cindy and Aaron picked me up for my return drive home in early March after my two-week stay at Spaulding Rehab Hospital. Aaron was a big help using a wheelchair to transport my belongings to the car. We stopped at the former Hilltop Steak House for lunch. I was excited to be homeward bound, but also nervous. I needed to be careful as I walked with crutches to not place any weight on my left leg. It was still winter in Maine, so I would have to be careful on the snow and ice. We were able to arrange for a visiting nurse a couple times a week, but the primary responsibility for care would fall on Cindy, after I had been in a hospital setting for two months. There would be a fair amount of medical care needed to change the dressing and treat the pin sites where the external fixator was screwed into my leg.

When we arrived home, Joel came rushing out to give me a hug. Sarah had worked all afternoon to pick up the living room and bake "welcome home" cupcakes. The room was decorated with signs saying, "Welcome home, Chris," and, "You've come a long way, baby!" Cindy, all the kids, and a few close friends were gathered to welcome me home. There were helium balloons and it was very festive.

We were blessed with wonderful support and offers of help from friends and members of the community. Meals were dropped off, our kids received offers for play dates or ski trips, friends offered to transport me to Boston for check-back appointments, and many other acts of kindness, including assistance with our daughter Sarah's financial aid application for college.

But behind the scenes it was difficult to witness the upheaval our family was experiencing. I was the visible victim, but the lives of everyone in the family had been upended. Uncertainty underlay everything. This would become even more evident in the coming months.

I watched Cindy and the kids carry the burden of waiting on me and taking care of the everyday household chores. They did this graciously, but it was difficult for me to be unable to help with the many things that needed attention.

I longed to be able to resume activities I had previously done. I could stand in the kitchen using my crutches while I heated water to make coffee. I then figured out that I could move the cup of coffee incrementally to the end of the counter and then be in a position to transfer it to the kitchen table without bearing weight on my left leg. This was a small victory.

I also did some foolish things in my zeal to resume previous activities. One day in March when the kids were in school and Cindy was shopping, I decided I would try to split some wood so we would have kindling for a fire. I hobbled outside with my crutches and somehow managed to bring a log and my splitting ax onto the snow-covered driveway. In an act of sheer stupidity, I laid my crutches down and tried to swing the ax while bearing my weight on my right leg. I lost my balance and fell. As I lay sprawled on the driveway, I was distraught, waiting for my left leg to start to scream in pain. Incredibly, this did not happen. Somehow I had not caused further injury to my leg. My next thought was panic that Cindy might return to see me sprawled on the driveway. I managed to get back up on my crutches and *hide* the evidence of my stupidity. I was exhausted when I got back in the house and realized how absolutely foolish (and how incredibly fortunate) I had been. It was only a long time later that I would tell Cindy about this.

I was on disability leave from my job, but one day a colleague picked me up to bring me in to my office so I could see my fellow workers. I decided to bring along the huge computer printout with my hospital bill from Mass General to turn in to our Health Trust claims unit. Unbeknownst to me, the staff had gathered in the large conference room to throw me a welcome-home surprise party. When I entered the room on my crutches, the nearly one hundred staff members greeted me with applause and banners welcoming me back. I was so surprised I was almost speechless. I ended up holding one end of the computer printout and tossing the printout across the room, telling them the length of this hospital bill might give them some idea of what I had been going through the past couple of months.

By outward appearances, I was doing well and had, indeed, made a lot of headway since the trauma of the accident on January 2. But there's more to the story. My March 10 journal entry reads:

> The adjustment to home has been quite a bit more difficult than I anticipated. It's been great to be home and see the kids, but I have gone through an emotional and psychological roller coaster. My leg has ached a lot—requiring me to go back to the stronger pain medication (Tylenol 3 with codeine) for a number of days. I think this might have affected my stomach and moods. Also, it's been extremely cold (sub-zero) and I wonder if the cold has also affected my leg—it seemed to improve as the temperatures became milder. It's difficult to be handicapped—to need people to do things for me. I'm trying to be better about allowing them to help, but it takes an effort.
>
> It's hard for me to see Cindy close to exhaustion—maintaining the household and having the additional burden of aiding me—but she really has been wonderful. We're trying to get the kids to help, even in small ways—despite their busy work and school schedules.

It might sound trivial, but I would get upset and frustrated waiting for return phone calls. It added to my sense of helplessness. I had been accustomed to be very busy and focused in my position as executive director of the Maine Municipal Association. It was a fast-paced office environment, and I could reasonably expect prompt responses to my requests. Now I found myself out of work, in pain, and reliant on others for even the most basic of tasks. I would leave messages and just have to wait for people to return my calls. I had to be careful to avoid tripping or falling as I moved around on crutches. My leg was very fragile, held together by the external fixator. I could not drive given the risk of injury to my leg and the safety issues involved. On top of all of this, my frustration and anger were deeply exacerbated by the legal issues surrounding the accident—more about that in the next chapter.

CHAPTER 7

Another Dimension

During my stay at Mass General, as I regained strength and my head cleared in between surgeries, I began to focus on the legal aspects of the accident. Although I was not a lawyer, I came from a family of attorneys and I also dealt with various legal issues in my work at the Maine Municipal Association. Initially I consulted with my brother Steve, a trial attorney in upstate New York. This was helpful, but I realized it would be important for me to retain an attorney in Maine, since all the proceedings would take place in Maine courts. Also, I generally had tried to separate business dealings from family or close friends. Steve concurred with my decision to retain an attorney in Maine and offered to be available as a sounding board if I had any questions.

I called several colleagues in Maine to ask them whom they would select for legal representation if they had been seriously injured in an accident. This gave me a good list of names. I then began making telephone calls from my hospital bed. This was a very interesting process, which resulted in my selection of an outstanding trial attorney who met with me in my hospital room a couple weeks after the accident. In the months that followed, I truly valued his excellent representation and sage counsel and support. I forged an excellent working relationship with him and his key associate. Their empathy and encouragement proved to be of immense help as I encountered a myriad of obstacles and frustrations dealing with the legal issues surrounding the accident.

I worked with my attorneys to file a civil lawsuit against the driver of the car that had struck me, but I also had a personal interest in keeping abreast of the handling of a possible traffic citation, and potentially participating as the case was adjudicated, given my understanding of the driver's significant history of traffic violations.

In the ensuing months I would learn several difficult lessons regarding insurance, civil litigation, and the criminal and traffic court system. The most eye-opening (and the cause of intense anger) was the manner in which I was closed out of any involvement in the traffic case. I made repeated calls to the district attorney's office to tell them of my injuries and my interest in being involved in the handling of the traffic case. It was my understanding that the driver had been charged with a relatively minor traffic violation. I was informed that there was not a role for me in the traffic case and that my remedy should be through a civil lawsuit.

Nonetheless, I contacted the district court to keep posted on the hearing date so I could attend when the case came before a judge to ensure it was made known that someone had been seriously injured in the accident. When I called on the day of the scheduled hearing in early June of 1989 to confirm the time and location, I was informed that the case had been pled the previous day for a $75 fine and no loss of license. The visiting judge who accepted the plea had not been informed by the district attorney's office that someone had been seriously injured in this incident. Consequently, the judge handled this as a routine case along with numerous other minor traffic violations that had been presented to him.

I was outraged. I wrote a letter expressing my anger to Governor McKernan with copies to the many prominent public officials who had expressed their concern after my accident. The *Maine Times*, a weekly newspaper in circulation at the time, decided to run a cover story entitled "Victim's Rights? Ask Chris Lockwood" in its edition for the week beginning August 11, 1989. The story provided a detailed insight into the handling of the traffic case and how I was made to feel the villain for my efforts to have a modicum of involvement.

It's my understanding the traffic case was eventually reopened and a larger fine and license suspension were imposed. Even more meaningful to me, I received a call from the visiting judge who handled the traffic case apologizing to me. He had read the *Maine Times* article and was distressed that he had not been informed that someone had been seriously injured. Had he known, it certainly would have affected his decision. I thanked him and told him how much it meant to me that he would pick up the phone and offer his apology.

There were other legal and insurance aspects that caused upset. In the civil case we were confronted by a situation in which the operator of the vehicle had the minimum liability insurance allowed by law. We also discovered that the uninsured and underinsured motorist coverage on my insurance policy was significantly less than the amount of liability coverage on my policy, due to an oversight when the policy changed to a different carrier and despite my efforts to maintain high levels of insurance protection. The uninsured and underinsured motorist coverage is designed to protect a person in the event he incurs injuries and damages that exceed the coverage offered by the other driver's insurance. This combination of circumstances resulted in a relatively small insurance recovery in view of the major injuries and medical expenses I incurred.

As a follow-up in subsequent years, I worked with legislators to revise Maine's insurance laws to require that the uninsured and underinsured motorist coverage is written at the same amount as the liability insurance unless the purchaser specifically requests a lower amount.

During the months after the accident, I was consumed by my quest for justice. Our lives had been totally upended. I was angry and felt an acute need for my family to see me stand up for myself. I was also in a state of denial regarding my anger. I initially scoffed at the suggestion that I might need to seek help from a counselor. I suspect that most people who know me would find it hard to imagine Chris Lockwood smashing his cane on the side of the barn or slamming his hand into a plaster wall, but these episodes reflected the anger that was raging inside me.

In terms of my anger, I finally heeded my wife's encouragement to seek counseling. This proved to be very important and therapeutic. Governor McKernan also appointed me to a citizens' advisory committee on victims' rights. This too provided a constructive outlet for my anger and enabled me to interact with families and individuals who had experienced great trauma, such as the murder or rape of a loved one. They all shared stories of having felt themselves victimized by the justice system, very similar to the way I felt closed out and disrespected by the manner in which the traffic case had been handled. This was an incredibly cathartic experience.

When I heard a legislative committee had scheduled a hearing to receive the recommendations of our advisory committee, I initially was not sure if I would attend or testify. But when I learned representatives of the prosecutors' organization planned to appear in opposition, I decided it would be important for me to participate. I had certainly testified in my professional capacity at many legislative committee hearings on municipal issues, but my testimony at this hearing on victims' rights was of a totally different nature. I did not have any prepared remarks—my testimony came straight from my heart and emotions. I spoke out on behalf of the families whom I had met through the advisory committee, seeking respect and dignity from those in the justice system. That evening I remember looking at myself in the mirror and feeling vindicated that I had stood up for myself and my family in the broader pursuit of justice.

There was another touch of humanity and respect which also was very meaningful. I learned that a judicial advisory commission was conducting a hearing regarding victims' rights and the judicial process. When I arrived in the late afternoon, the hearing had concluded and the members of the commission were preparing to leave. The justice chairing the commission noticed my arrival, and I explained I had hoped to offer some comments. She promptly reconvened the hearing to provide me an opportunity to testify. I genuinely appreciated the courtesy and respect she conveyed as I shared my experiences.

Years later, I have a better understanding of the tremendous drain I experienced from my anger and sense of victimization. I was consumed by negative energy and a sense of helplessness. It was a push-button issue—any mention of the accident and the traffic case would launch me. I did not realize it at the time, but I'm pretty sure I clung to this negative energy—I didn't want to let go, it would be "giving up." I was angry, and I needed to hold on to this anger and fury.

Sadly, as I look back on those early years, I realize my wife was the person who most often was in my company when I would launch. She had already endured so many trials herself, holding our family together and taking care of our everyday needs. She was physically and emotionally drained, yet she also was subjected to my tirades. As an aside, I came to recognize as time passed how seldom people would ask Cindy how she was doing—it's human nature to ask how the injured person is doing. I have tried to take this lesson to heart to be sure to ask how the caregiver is doing as well.

Intellectually I recognize how much energy is consumed by negative thoughts and anger, but I also am painfully aware of the powerful magnetic draw of these emotions.

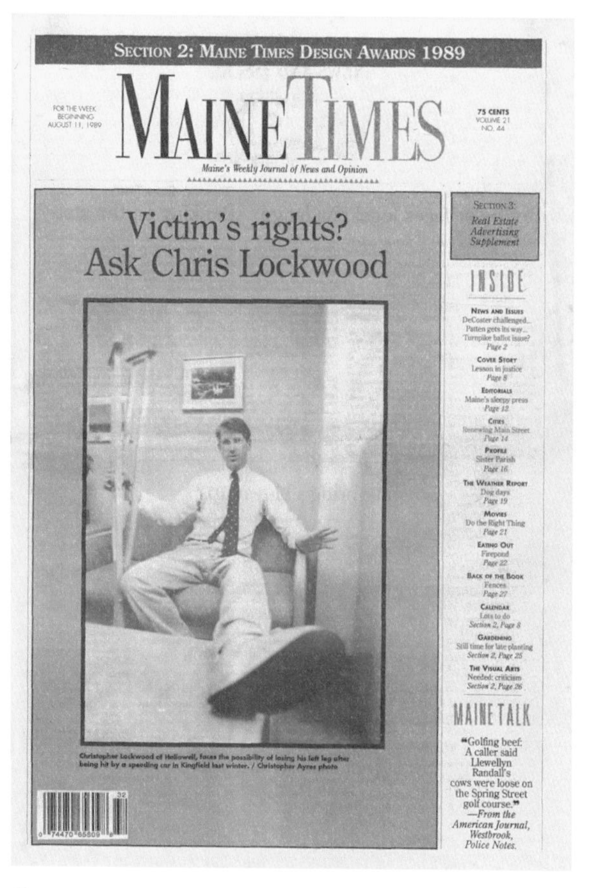

SECTION 2: MAINE TIMES DESIGN AWARDS 1989

FOR THE WEEK BEGINNING AUGUST 11, 1989

MAINE TIMES

Maine's Weekly Journal of News and Opinion

75 CENTS
VOLUME 21
NO. 44

Victim's rights?
Ask Chris Lockwood

Christopher Lockwood of Hallowell, faces the possibility of losing his left leg after being hit by a speeding car in Kingfield last winter. / Christopher Ayres photo

SECTION 3:
Real Estate Advertising Supplement

INSIDE

NEWS AND ISSUES
DeCoster challenged...
Patten gets its way...
Turnpike ballot issue?
Page 2

COVER STORY
Lesson in justice
Page 8

EDITORIALS
Maine's sleepy press
Page 12

CITIES
Renewing Main Street
Page 14

PROFILE
Sister Parish
Page 16

THE WEATHER REPORT
Dog days
Page 19

MOVIES
Do the Right Thing
Page 21

EATING OUT
Firepond
Page 22

BACK OF THE BOOK
Fences
Page 27

CALENDAR
Lots to do
Section 2, Page 8

GARDENING
Still time for late planting
Section 2, Page 25

THE VISUAL ARTS
Needed: criticism
Section 2, Page 26

MAINE TALK

"Golfing beef: A caller said Llewellyn Randall's cows were loose on the Spring Street golf course."
—*From the American Journal, Westbrook, Police Notes.*

Cover page, Maine Times, *week of August 11, 1989*

One victim's lesson in justice:

"I was made to feel the villain"

BY PAT NYHAN
Photography by Christopher Ayres

CHRISTOPHER LOCKWOOD is not naive. As director of the Maine Municipal Association for the past decade, he knows how the world works better than the average citizen. But when tragedy struck one snowy day last January, he began an odyssey into the criminal justice system that left him incredulous. As the victim of a car accident that may cost him his left leg, he was stunned to find out that, in fact, he had virtually no rights when it came to determining what happened to the speeding driver who blighted his life.

Lawyers regard Lockwood's incredulity as naive. Victim rights advocates say his reaction is typical: victims of auto accidents and violent crimes often feel as battered by the judicial system as by the act that propelled them into it. Lockwood has stubbornly insisted on participating in the outcome of his case, contacting everyone he could think of who could help, including the governor. To lawyers who say he should be focusing instead on recovering damages in a civil lawsuit against the driver, he responds that money isn't the issue, although he does plan to sue. His complaint has to do with recognition, access, and simple courtesy.

"Why do we have a justice system if people who are victims are squeezed out?" he asks.

Lockwood's stubbornness matches that of others across the country who have joined a growing victim rights movement. A decade ago, no states had victim rights laws on the books for criminal cases; now 45 do, including Maine. In that same time, victim service programs in prosecutors' offices have grown from a few hundred to 6,000 nationally, and federal support has broadened, according to John Stein, deputy director of the Washington-based National Organization for Victim Assistance.

"There's been an extraordinary level of change" in protection, Stein told *Maine Times*. Although civil traffic cases like Lockwood's don't get the same attention as criminal cases, and their victims can't usually take advantage of victim help programs, Stein predicts that someday they will.

Unfortunately, the rise in victims' demands coincides with a staggering increase in the burdens on courts and prosecutors' offices because of public demands to get tough on crime, raising a question: Who is going to pay for expanded victim services when the criminal justice system is barely coping now? (See related story.)

Maine's 1983 victim rights law requires that victims of crimes be notified of upcoming court hearings and allowed to testify. But in civil traffic cases such as Lockwood's, victims are largely left out of the process, especially since the vast majority of cases are handled through the mail when a defendant admits guilt and pays a fine. To Lockwood's amazement, judges deciding penalties in speeding cases often aren't even aware if an accident has occurred, or how bad a defendant's driving record may be.

Christopher Lockwood has learned the realities of the courts from a victim's perspective.

Excerpt from page 8, Maine Times, *week of August 11, 1989*
(Please see next page for the text of this article)

One victim's lesson in justice:

"I was made to feel the villain"

By Pat Nyhan
Photography by Christopher Ayres

CHRISTOPHER LOCKWOOD is not naïve. As director of the Maine Municipal Association for the past decade, he knows how the world works better than the average citizen. But when tragedy struck one snowy day last January, he began an odyssey into the criminal justice system that left him incredulous. As the victim of a car accident that may cost him his left leg, he was stunned to find out that, in fact, he had virtually no rights when it came to determining what happened to the speeding driver who blighted his life.

Lawyers regard Lockwood's incredulity as naïve. Victim rights advocates say his reaction is typical: victims of auto accidents and violent crimes often feel as battered by the judicial system as by the act that propelled them into it. Lockwood has stubbornly insisted on participating in the outcome of his case, contacting everyone he could think of to help, including the governor. To lawyers who say he should be focusing instead on recovering damages in a civil lawsuit against the driver, he responds that money isn't the issue, although he does plan to sue. His complaint has to do with recognition, access, and simple courtesy.

"Why do we have a justice system if people who are victims are squeezed out?" he asks.

Lockwood's stubbornness matches that of others across the country who have joined a growing victim rights movement. A decade ago, no states had victim rights laws on the books for criminal cases; now 45 do, including Maine. In that same time, victim service programs in prosecutors' offices have grown from a few hundred to 6,000 nationally, and federal support has broadened, according to John Stein, deputy director of the Washington-based National Organization for Victim Assistance.

"There's been an extraordinary level of change" in protection, Stein told the Maine Times. Although civil traffic cases like Lockwood's don't get the same attention as criminal cases, and their victims can't usually take advantage of victim help programs, Stein predicts someday they will.

Unfortunately, the rise in victims' demands coincides with a staggering increase in the burdens on courts and prosecutors' offices because of public demands to get tough on crime, raising a question: Who is going to pay for expanded victim services when the criminal justice system is barely coping now? (See related story.)

Maine's 1983 victim rights law requires that victims of crimes be notified of upcoming court hearings and allowed to testify. But in civil traffic cases such as Lockwood's, victims are largely left out of the process, especially since the vast majority of cases are handled through the mail when a defendant admits guilt and pays a fine. To Lockwood's amazement, judges deciding penalties in speeding cases often aren't even aware if an accident has occurred, or how bad a defendant's driving record may be....

—text from page 8, *Maine Times* August 11, 1989

CHAPTER 8

A Setback

Back to the medical side of things. Before I was discharged from Spaulding Rehab Hospital in late February, I had a check-back appointment with my doctors at Mass General. They indicated my leg looked good and scheduled me to return in mid-March to have surgery to remove the external fixator. They also invited me to participate in surgical grand rounds on June 1. I was not quite sure what might be entailed with grand rounds, but I understood it would be an opportunity for my doctors to discuss my case with other medical residents and interns. I took the invitation to be a positive sign of the headway I was making in light of the battery of surgeries I had undergone.

Little did I realize that the coming months would be a roller coaster of ups and downs, mostly downs.

I returned to Mass General in mid-March for the operation to remove the external metal fixator. After the surgery, Dr. O'Neill examined my leg to determine if the bone graft had taken hold. He held my ankle and pushed my leg to the side. Rather than the entire leg remaining rigid, the lower part of my leg moved to the side—it was like rubber below the knee. I was absolutely spooked. I had what was referred to as a "nonunion." He told me if the bone graft did not take hold in the next two months I would need to have a second operation. I appreciated his honesty, but I dreaded the thought of another graft.

In late March I returned to Boston to have a full-leg cast put on. It wasn't very comfortable, but it allowed me to start to bear weight on my left leg, which I hoped would help to stimulate healing of the bone tissue. I was also cleared to start physical therapy (PT) and to resume driving. Driving afforded me a degree of independence I had not had since the day of the accident. I still recall the first day I was able to drive on my own to do an errand and visit a friend.

The physical therapy proved to be very helpful in my rehabilitation. Over time I began to regain a certain amount of strength and mobility. I was experiencing a range of issues as a result of the various surgeries. In particular, the bone graft donor site on my lower back hurt terribly as I would lie in bed. I felt like I needed to be on a rotisserie when I slept to keep turning to try to find a comfortable position. I was very fortunate to have been assigned to a physical therapist by the name of Dana Melville. I did not realize at the time just how instrumental he would be in my rehabilitation and ongoing care.

As it turned out, surgical grand rounds were not to be. My sense of anxiety as the date of each check-back appointment approached turned out to be well founded. In late May a friend drove me to Mass

General. Dr. O'Neill determined that I still had a nonunion and that I would need a second bone graft. He explained that in cases such as mine (Type 3C cases), bones are the hardest aspect of healing. In reviewing case histories, he found it was not unusual to find patients who had undergone up to twenty surgeries over a three or four-year period and still lost their legs. I recalled a similar conversation with my lead doctor the day I arrived by helicopter at Mass General, but I had allowed myself to start believing the worst was behind me. The reality of this setback struck me really hard as I called Cindy to inform her I was being admitted to the hospital and would have a second bone graft operation the next day. I was in tears and very frightened.

The surgery was as rugged as I anticipated. I found myself in excruciating pain in a double room at Mass General. My roommate was a young boy from Armenia who had gone through major surgery and was also in terrible pain. He had many visitors and it was very difficult for me to get rest. Fortunately, some friends from Boston arranged to transport me to the airport on Memorial Day weekend to meet up with my friend John Madden, a private pilot, who flew me to Maine so I could recuperate at home.

It would be several months before we would know whether the operation had been successful. In the meantime, I faced an uncertain future that was complicated by the news that all the doctors who had been caring for me were completing their residencies and moving on to new positions. With this in mind, I transitioned to an orthopaedic surgeon who was on the regular staff at Mass General to ensure continuity of care in the coming months.

CHAPTER 9

Behind the Scenes

This is the hardest chapter for me to write. My journal brings back memories I would like to forget: incredible rage and frustration, fights among family members, fists being slammed into plaster walls, smashing and breaking my cane against the side of our barn, screaming arguments over seemingly trivial issues, and an overwhelming sense that our world had been turned upside down.

We're certainly not the first or only family to have experienced such trauma. What was hard to take at times was the incongruity of the outpouring of compassion at the initial news of the accident with the lack of understanding by some of the ongoing trauma and upheaval our family was experiencing in the months after the initial accident.

Our family was in crisis. The sons who had been with me at the time of the accident had thought their father might die. The lack of understanding by some people in the school system was particularly troubling and frustrating. It's difficult to know what is appropriate to write without pointing fingers or laying blame, but life in our home was compounded when one of our sons, who had been an A student prior to the accident, started to get failing grades and detentions. When we arranged a meeting at the school after I returned home from Mass General, it was like we were speaking to a brick wall. I honestly don't recall the specifics of our meeting, but I know I was ready to explode with the anger and frustration that had been building. We ultimately made the decision to send him to a private school the following year.

My journal provides glimpses of the upheaval our family experienced, but it is very difficult and painful for me to share specific examples. Just reading through my journal has been draining. Intense exchanges with screams from a family member: "You're not the only one affected by the accident!" Or one of our sons storming out of the room when asked, "How do you feel about Dad's accident?"

In the aftermath of one particularly scary episode when I tried to break up a fierce physical fight between two of my sons, I learned from talking with my oldest son that he was angry and terribly saddened that I wouldn't be able to play tennis with him again. He felt that his father had been taken away from him, in an important way. In an emotional and tender exchange, I told him how angry and saddened I was also. We wept together and embraced. When I related this incident in a subsequent personal counseling session, my counselor told me I had given a wonderful gift to my son.

Uncertainty hung over me and my family. Would I lose my leg? When would we get to a point that my health status was resolved? What did this mean for me professionally? I was not actively looking to make a professional change, but I was at a prime point in my career and would certainly entertain a possible move if the right opportunity arose. The accident brought this possibility to a screeching halt—the importance of maintaining continuity of health insurance coverage, uncertainty regarding my health status, questions regarding my stamina and ability to handle business travel and other responsibilities.

The salient point is the importance of recognizing that the ramifications of a serious injury are widespread among a family and are long-term.

CHAPTER 10

The Roller Coaster Continues

The summer and fall of 1989 turned out to be a "roller coaster" experience. I had returned to work after being out for four months, but I was very limited in my mobility. I had a long leg cast and used crutches to get around. I had little stamina and was discouraged at how exhausted I would become by the end of the day.

During the summer I developed a staph infection at one of the surgical sites on the outside of my leg. I was put on oral antibiotics, but the doctors kept close track out of concern that the infection might migrate into my bone tissue, which could cause serious complications. I had heard stories at Mass General of patients with injuries similar to mine who were still battling bone tissue infections years after their accidents.

The medical issues were interwoven with everyday life. We sought to find some normalcy as a family, but uncertainty regarding my health and my limitations were constant reminders that life was anything but normal. We became far more sensitized to physical obstacles which interfered with a handicapped person's freedom of mobility.

We decided to have the whole family travel by airplane to the state municipal league directors' summer workshop in Durango, Colorado. We were in for lessons in the lack of handicap accessibility and the trials and tribulations of traveling with a significant disability. Challenges included:

- Traversing long distances in airports to make flight connections
- The difficulties of using airplane rest rooms with a long leg cast
- The frustration of the condos for the conference lodging having a large flight of stairs to navigate on my crutches
- The lack of a public elevator in the resort leading to lower areas where functions were scheduled, necessitating a close friend in a wheelchair to have to use a service elevator and come through the kitchen

I was still in the early stages of adapting to the new reality of life with a disability—as well as the uncertainty of whether I might still end up losing my leg if the nonunion could not be healed. The following entry from my journal provides some insights:

> Just returning from an NLC convention in Atlanta—there's so much to try to put into the journal, but I seldom feel up to writing—it takes so much energy just to keep up with everyday life and work.

It's almost impossible to describe my feelings as far as my leg and adjusting to life with a disability. Maybe just a few examples help to illustrate.

Buffets—what used to be such a normal part of my life—especially at meetings—have taken on a whole new dimension. I need help to go through a buffet line. That's not a problem usually, when I'm with a group I know—people are more than willing to offer help, but it still eats away at my pride, my sense of self-sufficiency. But then there's the different situation I found at the hotel atrium restaurant—a breakfast buffet—I was by myself, trying to figure out how to manage—fortunately I was able to order off the menu, but I felt weak, odd.

At the conference, of course, I encountered many people who hadn't heard of the accident, and I had to go through endless explanations. And then there are the scores of questions and comments from people I'd meet in elevators, lobbies, etc.

Comments such as "What happened?" "A little early for skiing, isn't it?" "What did you do to yourself?" (That's a hard one to take). Then the toughest one to handle: "What happened to the other guy?" Without thinking about it, people can say the most innocent things that just stab at the pain, at the lifelong disability with which I'm trying to come to grips.

> So many people try to encourage by telling me how good I look—which I appreciate—but it's tough to be told how lucky I am or that they're glad I'm all right or that I'll be all right soon.

The roller coaster took another downturn at my check-back appointment in late summer when my cast was removed. To my dismay, I still had a non-union. The bones had not fused together. My Mass General doctor proposed an esoteric surgery using a variation of a bone-lengthening surgery pioneered by Dr. Gavriil Abramovich Ilizarov, a Soviet orthopaedic surgeon. Dr. Ilizarov had designed a device (somewhat similar to the external fixator that had held my leg together during the first couple of months) that could be used to lengthen a leg or arm bone very gradually by turning cranks on the device. My doctor at Mass General proposed attaching the Ilizarov device but using it to push the bones together rather than lengthening the bones—essentially a "reverse Ilizarov" surgery.

I was very concerned about undergoing more surgery, exposing myself to the risk of infection, as well as the uncharted territory in the proposed Ilizarov surgery. During this same period, my physical therapist (Dana Melville) provided me copies of medical journal articles he had obtained from a friend about the use of electrical magnetic stimulation to enhance the growth of bone tissue. Although I couldn't understand all the intricacies in the articles, I was intrigued with the underlying premise that electrical magnetic devices might stimulate the bone's natural healing process by sending low-level pulses of electromagnetic energy to the nonunion site.

I also arranged to get together with an acquaintance who had undergone an above-the-knee amputation as a teenager. I genuinely appreciated his willingness to talk with me and to share very personal insights into the difficulties he experienced. His explanation helped me to understand the differences, at least at that point in time, between an above-the-knee amputation compared to below-the-knee.

I sent a letter to my Mass General doctor in advance of my October appointment asking that we discuss all the possible options, including possible use of electrical magnetic stimulation, the Ilizarov surgery, and even amputation, as difficult as it was for me to put that option on the list. As we discussed the various options during the appointment, my doctor explained that electrical magnetic stimulation would involve wearing a device over the nonunion site for eight hours a day for three or four months. Although my doctor explained there was not definitive research on this subject, I told him I was willing to take the time to pursue electrical stimulation before I underwent any more surgery. To his credit, my doctor ordered an electrical magnetic stimulation device, even though, as I understood, Mass General did not generally subscribe to the efficacy of electrical stimulation during that time period. In the late fall of 1989 I began wearing the electrical stimulation device every night as I slept.

When I returned to Mass General in early January, it appeared that the bones might be starting to unite, but we would need to wait a couple more months to be sure. By this time, I had been fitted with a long leg brace, which allowed for partial weight bearing, and I had started to use a cane to assist in getting around. I continued to strap the electrical stimulation device to the nonunion area every night as I slept.

CHAPTER 11

Connecting with a Rehab Doctor

It had been a little over a year since the accident, and it was still unclear whether I would end up losing my leg. I was back at work but was having a range of medical and physical issues. I wanted desperately to be whole again and to do things I had done prior to the accident.

I decided to see if I could cross-country ski. I put on my skis in our front yard and took a couple of laps. Physically I was able to ski, although my left leg kept veering to the outside due to the angle at which my leg was reattached after the surgery. On my second lap I slipped and fell. As I lay on the ground I was very worried that I might have injured my leg, but fortunately that was not the case. On the other hand, I later learned from my rehab doctors that my leg was probably at a very vulnerable stage in the healing process and that I was fortunate that I had not undone much of the restorative work that had been done during the past year.

I continued to have trouble getting a good night's sleep. I would get very tired and didn't have much stamina by the end of the afternoon. I was frustrated and angry, although I was trying to contain my anger.

My physical therapist suggested that I see Dr. James Fegan, a physiatrist located in Waterville, Maine. I had never heard of a physiatrist, but I learned they are medical doctors (MD's) who specialize in rehabilitation medicine.

As it turned out, Dana had an ulterior motive in recommending Dr. Fegan (more on that later). In any event, I finally decided to call Dr. Fegan's office to make an appointment, but was told that I needed to get a referral from my doctor. I called my orthopaedic surgeon at Mass General. He questioned why I wanted to see a physiatrist. He said they worked with stroke victims. I told him that I was dealing with a lot of issues, in addition to my injured leg, and that my physical therapist thought it would be a good idea. He agreed to make the referral.

My appointment with Dr. Fegan was scheduled for late afternoon. I considered cancelling the appointment. I had spent so much time in doctors' offices over the past year, and I didn't know if this appointment would be worthwhile. To my great fortune, I kept the appointment.

I was Dr. Fegan's last appointment of the day. He spent two hours with me, listening to me discuss the accident and learning about my life before the accident. The floodgates on my anger and frustration were blown open during that appointment: my anger that I would never play tennis again even though my son Nate and I had just gotten to the point of having competitive matches, feeling helpless and handicapped as my wife held down the fort and I was so limited in my ability to do things around the house or to interact with my kids as I had previously done. It was only at the very end of the appointment that Dr. Fegan said, "Oh, yes, I probably should look at your leg."

I realized after the appointment that this was the first time since the accident that I had poured out all the emotions and anger that had been building up for the past year. Here was a doctor who took the time to listen, who could understand the frustration and anger of a physically active and competitive forty-three-year-old man who had been seriously injured in an accident. This was the first of a series of appointments over the course of the next year in which I worked with Dr. Fegan.

It was after this initial appointment that I learned my physical therapist's ulterior motive in connecting me with Dr. Fegan. Jim Fegan had not initially gone into medicine as a career. He had been a jet fighter pilot in Vietnam. He incurred a major leg injury when his plane was shot down. He experienced a number of frustrations during his rehabilitation and decided to enter medicine with a desire to treat the whole person rather than just a part of a person. He and I were essentially in the same age bracket. He was an athletic, competitive individual who could totally relate to my experience and understood it was not sufficient to tell me that I needed to find some sedentary activities as a replacement.

CHAPTER 12

Life-Changing Advice

The timing of my connection with Dr. Fegan was incredibly serendipitous. I was anxious to get back to doing things I had done previously. I was very self-conscious about my appearance, about what other people would think, about "overcoming" my disability. I was unsure what risks I should take and was certainly focused on the short term. I began meeting with Dr. Fegan on a regular basis.

A few months later at my check-back appointment with my orthopaedic surgeon, I received the wonderful news that the bones in my left leg had united. I would still have an ongoing disability, but healing the non-union was crucial to allow me to avoid an above-the-knee amputation. It was not possible to identify the precise reason for the success. It may have been partial weight bearing over a period of months, positive attitude, the electrical stimulation device, or a combination of all these factors, but I believe the electrical stimulation device had a significant role. With this news, I was able to move to a shorter brace that would allow me to have more mobility and open the possibility of engaging in more physical activities. How incredibly fortunate for me I had the benefit of Dr. Fegan's wise counsel and advice at this critical juncture.

One of Dr. Fegan's initial recommendations was that I try swimming and walking in the shallow end of a pool. I still recall how self-conscious I was as I went from the locker room to the pool on my crutches, wondering if I would freak people out with my disfigured leg. When I shared this experience with Dr. Fegan, he reassured me that the swimming and exercise in the pool would help to strengthen my leg and facilitate my rehabilitation. He told me that although it was understandable that I might be self-conscious, what other people might think was their issue, not my issue.

During my subsequent appointments, Dr. Fegan provided incredibly wise counsel. He helped me to understand that I didn't need to complete a decathlon to be successful. Just to live an active daily life would be a big achievement. I didn't have to prove anything to anyone but myself. I had been discouraged at how exhausted I would be by the end of a day. He helped me to understand that daily routine activities, such as getting in and out of a car, were requiring me to expend 20–30% more energy than prior to the accident.

Perhaps most importantly, he provided a framework for me to make decisions that would serve me well over the long term. He offered a couple of metaphors that have stayed with me:

- He told me to imagine I had a car with 120,000 miles on it and I wanted to get it to last 200,000 miles. If I took it on the back roads and beat the daylights out of it, I wouldn't make 200,000 miles. But if I took it on the better roads most of the time and only went on the back roads when I needed to, I could make 200,000 miles. As an example, if I had a choice between stairs or an elevator, take the elevator. I needed to make decisions that were right for me. I didn't need to prove anything to anyone else. I really needed to hear this advice.

- The other metaphor was that I had a bank account with a certain amount of money. It could only be drawn down once. There would not be any more deposits. I needed to be thoughtful about how I expended the funds (my physical condition).

How did this apply to me? Here was my situation as Dr. Fegan explained: I was forty-three years old. During the coming years my right leg would be the workhorse for my injured left leg and I would likely develop arthritis in various parts of my body. Given the location of the injury on my left leg, it would not be possible to do a knee replacement. I needed to get as much mileage out of my body as I could. I needed to think for the long term. I had choices. I needed to make decisions that were right for me. I didn't need to prove anything to anyone else. The used car and bank account metaphors were very helpful in putting my situation into very understandable terms.

Among other things, I have what's known as "foot drop." Many of the nerves and muscle tissue in my left leg were destroyed. I can push my foot down, but I can't pull it back up. I have sensation and feeling in my left leg, but it's somewhat reduced. I have reasonably good circulation, but I need to be careful about swelling and be watchful of frost bite or freezing in colder temperatures.

To compensate for the foot drop on my injured left leg, I wear a brace, an ankle foot orthosis (AFO), which fits inside my footwear and pushes up the bottom of my foot so I have a more normal stride. If I walk without the brace, my foot drags and I limp noticeably and I am more likely to trip when my foot catches or hits something. The brace is functional, but it can become uncomfortable in certain positions and can lead to various problems as my foot hits it or rubs against it.

One of the important decisions I made was to use a cane to get around. I had never given any thought to using a cane, how to use it, why it might help. I must admit there also was a certain stigma I think I associated with using a cane. I certainly didn't grasp that using a cane might be a key strategy to allow me to have a more active and satisfying life style over the long haul. No, in the early going it was a reminder of my disability. There was a proud part of me that longed for a day when I no longer would need to use a cane. I viewed discontinuing the use of a cane as one of the mile-markers on my road to recovery.

I also didn't realize there are some very important practical aspects of using a cane. First of all, which arm should I use? My natural inclination was to use my left arm since I had a left leg injury. Wrong, very wrong. I needed to have the cane on my right side so that I could shift my weight to my right arm as I took a forward stride with my left leg. That really took some practice, but the whole idea was to allow me to regain a more normal stride while reducing the wear and tear on my injured leg. Using a cane also helps to provide some stability, particularly if the terrain is uneven or slippery, but in my case it's especially geared to lessening wear and tear and allowing for a more normal gait.

It is also important to have the cane be the correct length. I was instructed that the top of the cane should be level with the middle of my wrist as I was standing upright. Since the cane will be placed two or three feet in front of me as I take a stride, I can comfortably shift my weight onto the cane without having to stoop too low.

Having learned these practical tips, I have observed situations on TV shows or in plays in which actors limp along, holding the cane on the same side as the injured leg or using a cane that is too short. As a result, the individual has to stoop over or just take one slow step after another.

When my friend Ted Vaughan brought me a beautiful handmade Amish cane, it was too long. I joked with Ted that I was very proud of myself for knowing the correct end to saw to cut it down to size!

I was quite self-conscious when I initially graduated from crutches and started using a cane. This was about a year after the accident. A female town councilor who was about my age saw me at a meeting at my office and asked how I was doing. I told her I was getting along

OK, but that I would have a permanent disability and I would be using a cane. She said that she thought men with canes were sexy! I gave her a big hug and told her that was the best thing she could have told me.

Dr. Fegan was very pragmatic. During one of my appointments, I told him about how much my lower back hurt me as a result of the two bone graft surgeries, in which bone tissue had been taken from the back of each of my hips to try to repair the destruction of bone in my left leg. Dr. Fegan suggested that I try wearing suspenders (braces). At my next appointment, I complained about my back again and Dr. Fegan asked if I had followed up on his suggestion. I had not, so I had my assignment. I found some suspenders and had buttons sewn into my suit pants. This was the start of a new look for me, and most importantly, relief from the discomfort caused by the pressure of a belt on the bone graft sites. It didn't provide instantaneous relief, but certainly made a difference over time.

Dr. Fegan's advice wasn't rocket science but has proven incredibly valuable. His focus on looking at the long term radically changed my perspective. When I tell people about the used car metaphor, they sometimes ask what the better roads are. The better roads are using aids to lessen the wear and tear of everyday routine activities, taking an elevator instead of the stairs, using a cane for walking to and from my car to go to a store or walking through a supermarket or an airport, using a handicap placard, making thoughtful decisions about priorities, what's important enough to risk possible injury or wear and tear.

Clearly I could walk through a supermarket without a cane, but I would start to feel it very quickly in my leg and my back. It would also be additional wear and tear on my entire body and use a bit more energy, all of which accumulates over time. This is exactly what Dr. Fegan was referring to: Use the better roads for everyday activities to lessen the wear and tear on my body.

In terms of risk, Dr. Fegan suggested that I consider using snow shoes with poles as an outdoor winter activity. This would involve far less risk than skiing, in which my foot would be locked into a binding and the torque could reinjure my leg if I were to fall.

CHAPTER 13

Never Again?

The Last Time
I cannot remember the last time I played tennis.
I only know that now, because of "the accident," I will never play tennis again.
I'm learning to adjust, to look at things I'm able to do, rather than dwelling on those that I cannot do.
But it's painful, it's rugged, to see a tennis court or to be reminded of things in my past that I took too much for granted.
Even as I write this, I realize there are many things in my life that I take for granted.

Journal—Christopher Lockwood
May 23, 1990

Although my work with Dr. Fegan was very helpful, the above journal entry reflects the sadness and angst I felt about not ever being able to play tennis again. I honestly did not believe it would be possible.

In another example of the warped Lockwood sense of humor, my brother Bert called during this time to ask how I was doing. I told him that I was getting along fairly well overall, but I confided how hard it was for me to accept that I would never play tennis again. Bert's classic response: "Look at it this way, Chris, you were never very good, anyway!"

My son Nate was in his senior year of high school in 1991. It was bittersweet for me when I would go to watch his tennis matches. I would be happy to see him play, but inside I would feel anger and sadness. On one particular day, Nate invited me to come onto the court to hit a couple of balls in between matches. To my surprise, my stroke was still fairly strong, although I certainly could not move very well on the court.

I wasn't quite sure what to expect when I told Dr. Fegan at my next appointment about having hit the tennis ball with my son. He told me he wasn't concerned, especially in contrast to an activity such as skiing in which my leg would be locked into a binding. He explained that the worst thing that might happen would be that I would fall and scrape myself up. I would have to decide if it was too frustrating not being able to run or to cover enough court.

When I initially considered that it might be possible for me to get back to playing tennis, I wondered to myself, "What will people think? Why does he use a cane if he can play tennis?"

When I expressed my concern to Dr. Fegan, he looked me directly in the eyes and said, "It doesn't matter what other people think. You need to make decisions that are right for you."

What a gift! I really needed to hear this direct response. Many years later it seems very obvious to me, but at the time I had a huge mental barrier about what other people might think. Dr. Fegan's advice was instrumental in helping me to regain a level of activity that I thought would not be possible. This is why I have decided to write this book. If I can share this advice to make a difference for even one person, I will feel that I've passed along the wonderful gift that was given to me.

Lockwood with a forehand stroke August 2018

CHAPTER 14

Getting Back to Tennis

With Dr. Fegan's encouragement, I gradually started my reentry into tennis. Initially I played with my sons and daughter. After a while I was invited by some friends to sub for one of the regulars in their men's doubles group. I was somewhat nervous about how I would do, but I was buoyed by an outing in which I felt I had held my own. More invitations came and eventually I became a regular member of the group.

As I got back into playing tennis, I realized I needed to adapt my game. Clearly my mobility is limited. I cannot run and cover the court like I had previously done. I am in a different zone mentally when I get onto the court. I need to stay focused on where I would like to hit the ball and where I need to be to play the next shot. I primarily play doubles, which doesn't require me to cover as much court as playing singles.

I'm right handed and have developed a strong top spin forehand stroke, jokingly referred to as "the howitzer" by my playing companions. I bear most of my weight on my good leg. I shuffle to either side as I'm moving to get to a ball. I can move more quickly to my right side, but if I need to move to my left (my

On the tennis court with brace on left leg—August 2018

backhand), I sometimes switch my racquet to my left hand to afford myself a little more reach to return a ball. One of my playing companions will often yell, "Wrong hand!" or jokingly say, "That's illegal," all part of the camaraderie of our group.

I'm blessed that I've linked up with a wonderful group of people who love the game of tennis. When I initially was getting back into playing, I made a point of briefly explaining my injury when I was playing with new people and asked them to play their regular game. If they want to hit a drop shot or a lob, that's fine. If I get to it, I feel good, but I don't want folks to modify their game or apologize. I don't have to worry about apologies for drop shots or lobs in my regular groups! It's all part of the fun of being on the court.

One of the most meaningful events in my early return to tennis was having the chance to play with my son Nate in a local "Whatever Week" summer tennis tournament. We made it to the finals, coming in as runners-up. It was the first and only time I ever won a trophy for a sporting event, but far more importantly, it was something I thought I would never be able to do with him again after the accident.

During one of the first years after I had gotten back to playing tennis, I was on a trip in the San Diego area staying at a resort with tennis courts. I somewhat nervously put my name on a list at the pro shop to try to line up a game, preferably doubles. I received a call from a young man asking if I would like to play singles. When we met on the court, I explained my situation and said I would try to play singles, although I primarily played doubles since I couldn't cover as much court given my leg injury. I encouraged him to play his regular game. We had a good match and I was fairly sure I had held my own. The affirmation came the next day when he called and asked me to play again. This was a real boost to my self-confidence on the tennis court.

It's truly a gift to be back playing tennis. As I look back on the conversation with Dr. Fegan about my concern with what people might think, I am so thankful for his straightforward advice. Now when I tell people about the accident and that I use a cane to get around, but that I've gotten back to playing tennis, I joke that I use a tennis racquet, not a cane, on the court.

CHAPTER 15

Ongoing Maintenance

Dr. Fegan's used car metaphor was certainly apropos; the importance of reducing wear and tear over the long term to extend the lifespan of a physical body that will develop various problems and injuries over time proved invaluable.

It's remarkable for me to look at the routine activities associated with everyday living—getting in and out of a car, walking from a parking lot to and from a store, walking through a supermarket, walking my dog, etc. I could do each of these activities without using a cane, but my leg would start to hurt, particularly given the impact of my foot against the brace, and other parts of my body would also experience the wear and tear. That would be just after a single day. Multiply these daily activities over the thirty years since the accident and it amounts to 10,950 days. That's a lot of wear and tear just for routine activities. So my use of a cane is a key part of my strategy to get as much mileage as possible.

Another part of the strategy is working with a wonderful group of medical professionals who are committed to aiding me in achieving the goal of leading an active lifestyle over the long term consistent with Dr.

Fegan's metaphor of the used vehicle. My primary care doctor and my naturopathic doctor are very supportive of this long-term strategy and have helped me enlist other medical professionals to assist in providing "routine maintenance" and specialized attention as needed.

The doctors at Mass General did an amazing job saving my left leg so I could have reasonable functionality; however, my left leg has some unusual characteristics which cause ongoing problems. My leg flairs to the left and the front outside bottom of my foot pushes downward significantly lower than the rest of my foot. This creates a lot of pressure on the bottom and outside of my foot as it hits the brace I wear to compensate for the foot drop. This causes callous buildups and other issues. I have also developed arthritis in certain joints and plantar fasciitis on both feet. I have been fortunate to link up with podiatrists who use conservative treatment methods to keep me functioning with routine maintenance visits.

A few years ago when I was experiencing problems with my brace, as well as other foot and leg issues, my podiatrist referred me to a different orthotist who was the first to do a comprehensive evaluation, rather than just focusing on my injured leg. He observed my right leg was basically the "workhorse" and that I was "out of alignment." In addition to designing a new brace for my left leg, he molded an orthotic insert for my right foot. This helped to alleviate some of the recurring problems I had been experiencing.

I've maintained a connection with Dana Melville, my long-time physical therapist. At the direction of my podiatrist, Dana periodically treats my chronic plantar fasciitis and other foot issues. When I mentioned Dr. Fegan's used car metaphor to Dana, he joked that it was too bad he couldn't find a "grease fitting" as he was applying ultra sound to an arthritis build-up in my toe joint.

I also experience pain and discomfort in various areas of my body as a result of the many surgeries and the normal wear and tear from an active lifestyle. I have found massage therapy to be very helpful, particularly on my lower back on the donor sites for the bone grafts, along the scar lines for the surgeries, and on my feet and legs, which take quite a pounding.

Without overdoing the used car metaphor, it's clear that all of the above connections and activities are similar to the steps needed to do ongoing maintenance and to avoid unnecessary wear and tear to extend the useful life of the vehicle to reach the 200,000-mile mark.

Out for a walk in the Vaughan Woods, Hallowell, October, 2018

CHAPTER 16

Thirty Years Later

It's been thirty years since the accident. How has my life changed? Do I look at things differently? In some ways, these are difficult questions to answer. After all, I've been dealing with the accident and its consequences since it happened. How can I discern what I might be doing differently or how I might view the world from a different perspective? But then again, it's fair to take a few steps back for reflection on lessons learned, on possible changes in attitude, on physical pursuits, and perhaps on life itself.

I'd like to be able to say that I'm a totally different person as a result of the accident—that I cherish every moment, that I consider every time I step onto a tennis court as a gift, that I never resent the injuries I incurred or my ongoing disability. But of course I am human and subject to the emotions and frailty facing all of us.

On the other hand, I honestly believe I have developed a different outlook on things. It wasn't a grand epiphany, but rather it evolved over time. Somewhere along the way, I made the change from focusing on things I was not able to do to embracing the things I am able to do. Clearly, getting back to playing tennis was the key part of this evolution. It's hard for me to fathom making such a profound shift in focus if I had not been able to get back to playing the sport I loved the most. I have deep admiration for individuals who are able to shift their focus in a positive direction despite not being able to get back to doing something they truly loved. With that said, I do believe I consider it a gift each time I get onto the tennis court. Sometimes I might wish I had played better, but in my heart I am just thankful that I have been able to get back to doing something I love.

Thirty years later I don't think about the accident much, but every so often it flashes back when I hear the sound of sirens or if the weather conditions remind me of that chilly January day. I certainly think about the accident on January 2, the anniversary. The first year I was able to play tennis after the accident, I wrote letters to Dr. Fegan and another doctor who was treating me to tell them that I had played tennis on the anniversary and to thank them for their counsel and support. I generally try to arrange a tennis match on the anniversary as a way to focus on the positive, all in line with my realization that I'll never get over the accident, but I can try to move forward rather than dwelling in the past.

Writing this book has certainly provided the opportunity for reflection. It was painful and sobering to read my journal entries and recall the many surgeries, the ups and downs, the upheaval in our family, the uncertainty of what might lie ahead, and the interference with pursuing new professional opportunities, as well as coming to grips with a permanent partial disability.

One of the major lessons I learned, and which I hope to pass on to others, is the importance of taking a *long-term approach* when facing rehabilitation after a serious injury or accident. I certainly did not have a long-term outlook. I was bound and determined to become as active as possible, to prove to others that I had "beaten the odds." It would not have occurred to me to look ten, twenty, or thirty years down the road as I made decisions about what activities to consider. It was only as a result of Dr. Fegan's counsel, with the used car and bank account metaphors, that I stopped to consider the wear and tear over the long haul. This really leaped out at me recently when I was visiting longtime friends in the Pacific Northwest. Each day we would go on long walks with their golden retriever. During my visit we had discussed the first draft of my book, and I had explained the value of using a cane. It then struck me that there wouldn't be any way that I could have, or would have wanted to, go on these daily walks without the cane. As it was, my left foot started to hurt from the constant impact with my brace, but I truly value the ability to get good physical exercise each day.

I'm thankful I had the benefit of such sage advice at a crucial time during the early stage of my rehabilitation. My pride and ego were strong at work. I had a goal of getting rid of the cane as soon as I could, as a milestone in my "recovery." Had I followed this approach, I'm very certain I would not be nearly as active, or as content, as I am now thirty years after the accident. It might be hard to believe, but a simple strategy of using a cane has been instrumental in enabling me to maintain an active lifestyle over this extended period of time.

Has this experience changed me in other ways? Perhaps, although it's more difficult to discern changes in attitudes and viewpoints compared to physical activities. I certainly believe I am more sensitive to accessibility issues and to victims. During winter months I notice impassable sidewalks as people with disabilities or without vehicles are forced onto roadways and handicap ramps are blocked. The same is true when I observe obstacles in buildings that impair the access of a person in a wheelchair or with some other handicap. I recently visited a restaurant that had undergone extensive remodeling but did not have a bathroom that could be accessed by someone in a wheelchair. I brought this to the attention of the restaurant manager.

My experience after the accident was my first encounter as a victim, as far as I can recall. What an incredibly powerful experience this was. I had always been accustomed to being in a fair amount of control, having the ability to have a say and to influence things that affected me. What an eye opener! I don't believe I had ever experienced such a sense of outrage. I wish I still had a copy of the letter I sent to the governor after the traffic case was closed without any opportunity for me to participate or without any disclosure that someone had been seriously injured. I recall that it started out, "It is with a sense of absolute outrage that I write to you...."

This certainly has made me very sensitive to the plight of victims and the issue of victims' rights. I haven't made this a top priority, especially given other challenges in my life, but I hope that this book helps to shed some light on this issue.

The accident was truly traumatic and changed my life and those of my family forever. I will never get over the accident, but hopefully by sharing this story I will pass along the wonderful support and advice that has allowed me to regain such a meaningful level of activity, especially getting back to playing tennis.

So here in summary are my takeaways:

- Make decisions based on what is best for you and block out concern about what other people might think. This might not sound very important, but I believe our pride and much of what we experience in our society can affect our decision-making. I have seen this when I've encouraged acquaintances who have incurred serious injuries to consider using a cane. Does our pride get in the way of using an aid that might alleviate some of the wear and tear and help us to be more active?
- Take a long-term view. This has made a huge difference in my ability to maintain an active lifestyle in the thirty years since the accident.
- Be your own advocate. The lessons my wife and I learned in dealing with a major health crisis certainly equipped us well as we faced other serious medical issues in more recent years.

Obtain as much information and knowledge as possible so you can work together with your medical team. We also developed some pragmatic practices that have served us well over the years:

- Keeping a notebook to keep track of items discussed in appointments and items to remember to discuss in future appointments
- Preparing a list of items to discuss in advance of an upcoming appointment and bringing copies of the list to give to the doctor/nurse practitioner
- If possible, having a second person in the appointment to take notes and serve as a second set of ears
- Keeping an updated list of medications
- Keeping a list of surgeries/diseases, with dates, to assist in filling out medical history forms and also to assist your offspring in compiling family medical history

Finally—reflections on life itself. More than anything else I have come to value the importance of family, to cherish time together, to be thankful for special people in my life, for their love and support, and for the level of activity I have been able to regain after an accident that changed my life and those of my family forever.

I am indebted to the scores of people who helped and encouraged me throughout the years, most particularly to my family. Thank you.

Acknowledgments

There are many people I wish to acknowledge.

For valuable observations and suggestions on early drafts of the book: Ted and Carolyn Vaughan, Laurie Furlong, Joel and Shannon Lockwood, Eric Conrad, Sue Walters, and John Aromando, Esq.

For suggestions on the title: Geoff Herman and Joel Lockwood.

To my family and friends and the staff of Maine Authors Publishing for their patience as I wrestled with a subtitle.

For medical support and encouragement: Ron & Becky Morin and the paramedics and crew of Sugarloaf Ambulance/Rescue, the staffs of the Massachusetts General Hospital and Spaulding Rehabilitation Hospital, Brian Ridge (MD), Daniel O'Neill (MD), Jeffery Fearon (MD), Elaine Woo (MD), Dana Melville (PT), James Fegan (MD), the late Carol Eckert (MD), Kathryn Wistar (MD), Anne Jacobs (ND), Daniel Buck (DPM), Michael Kipp (DPM), Laurie Furlong (massage therapist), David Johnson (CO).

For legal counsel and support: Ralph Lancaster, Esq., and John Aromando, Esq.

For camaraderie and good fun: All of my tennis compatriots—too many to list.

I am truly thankful for the incredible love and support of my family and friends. It has been and continues to be quite the journey!